AF – for Amélie and Eloise

JB – for Sam and Alice

There came a day when
Jack felt sad –
his mum was tired, her
heart felt bad.

She said that soon
she'd not be there,
to wash his face and
brush his hair.

"I'll have to leave this
place, my love,
and sleep with angels
up above."

Jack searched her face,
but couldn't tell –
would Mummy take her
love as well?

"When I'm gone, you
and Dad
can talk about the
fun we had."

But Jack sat down and
thought that day,
would Mummy take
her love away?

So, snuggled down,
when it felt right,
Jack asked Mummy
late that night,
"Who will love me
when you're gone?"

She pulled him
close and told
her son...

"My love for you can never leave,
it's like the sun, the air you breathe.
It lives inside us both, you know,
and like you it will always grow."

"So, when you cannot see my face
or hear my voice around this place,
just close your eyes and you will hear me say...
I LOVE YOU
loud and clear."

"And even though I will be gone,
the stars at night will sing my song.
The wind will fly me through the sky
and tell the tale of you and I."

"You'll see me, Jack,
in all you do.
When Daddy smiles,
I'll be there too!"

"When you're at school
and when you play,
I'll be the sun that
warms your day."

And so, at last, Jack took her hand,
and felt that he could understand
the kind of love that fills her heart
will make him shine when they're apart.

They sat together for a while,
with shining eyes and peaceful smiles.
"I love you, Jack, I love you so."
Jack held her close and said, "I know."

The End

Mindfulness Exercises

Take some time now to enjoy this moment,
be present and relax.

Find some space on the floor,
lie down and imagine you have a
tiny white feather in your hand.

Breathe in deeply then see if you can blow
your feather all the way to the stars.

Keep trying until it gets there!

Now, turn towards each other ... and
blow each other a kiss!

Find a space and get comfortable – you
could be sitting on the floor, in the garden,
having a cuddle or lying down.

Just be happy.

Now, breathe.

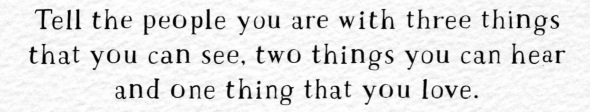

Look around.

Tell the people you are with three things
that you can see, two things you can hear
and one thing that you love.

Close your eyes and spend one minute thinking
about the best day of your life.

Try and remember it in as much detail as possible.

If you like, you can share this with the people
you are with right now.

Where to Find Help

Scary Mommy
15 Meaningful Grief and Loss Activities to Help Kids Cope with Death
https://tinyurl.com/366x59kc

Winston's Wish
Supporting a Bereaved Child
https://tinyurl.com/5bpu2s38

Young Minds
Supporting Your Child with Grief and Loss
https://tinyurl.com/24rp6k6t

Cancer.Net
Helping Grieving Children and Teenagers
https://tinyurl.com/kjux34yr

Space for Doodles

Can you draw a picture of how you feel?

Things We Love Doing with Our Family

Write them down or draw a picture

Anna Friend

Anna is a writer, director and actor.
She has spent the last ten years creating performances
for children with her company, Quirky Bird Theatre.
She is a mum to two boys, Jack and Billy.

The COVID-19 pandemic offered Anna the time to
develop the Big Little Hearts books, a series written
to support families dealing with traumatic life events.
The books use honest, simple language designed to
start conversations and provide comfort.

She lives in Wiltshire with her family.

Jake Biggin

Jake is an artist and illustrator. He studied Fine Art
at Central St Martins in London. A father of two,
Jake works in a little box at the end of his garden,
which currently doubles as a classroom.

About Big Little Hearts

This series has been created to help children
understand and deal with pivotal moments in their lives.

In Memory of Ellen Wollaston-Cooper

Ellen was a woman who lived a life full of love, creativity, passion and joy.

In 2015, she was diagnosed with breast cancer and from that point on fought for life with a fierceness that inspired me and so many others. Between her initial diagnosis and her death in 2018 she not only raised awareness and a huge amount of money for Cancer Research UK, she told her story, made us laugh (a lot), created truths (that I still live by today) and faced death with honesty.

And she loved hard.

At the heart of all of it was her family, her two children, Amélie and Eloise, and husband, Bryan. Throughout it all, she continued to be the driving force, the beating heart of the family and although it must have been one of the hardest things she ever did, included her children in the journey she was on.

And it was this, her amazing way of facing the inevitable that inspired me to write this book. Through her, I have realized that death, whenever it comes, does not need to be feared. Although we will always be sorry to leave those we love, what Ellen taught me is what's most important is whilst we have the gift of life, we make it count. The final words must be hers: "Don't waste a single second. Love hard, be kind. Make every moment count. No excuses!"

PILLGWENLLY
16/2/27

Anna Friend